BURLESQUES

FROM CORNHILL TO GRAND CAIRO

AND

JUVENILIA

BY

WILLIAM MAKEPEACE THACKERAY

With Illustrations by the Author, George Cruikshank, and Richard Doyle

London

MACMILLAN AND CO., Limited

NEW YORK : THE MACMILLAN COMPANY

1903

NOTE

A Legend of the Rhine was originally serialised in *George Cruikshank's Table Book* during 1845, when it was illustrated by the editor. It was reprinted in *Jeames's Diary, A Legend of the Rhine*, and *Rebecca and Rowena* (Appleton's Popular Library of the Best Authors, New York, 1853), and in *Miscellanies* (vol. 3 ; London, 1856).

Rebecca and Rowena (1850) is a much altered version of *Proposals for a Continuation of Ivanhoe, In a Letter to Monsieur Alexandre Dumas, by Monsieur Michael Angelo Titmarsh*, which appeared in *Fraser's Magazine*, vol. 34, pp. 237-245, 359-367 (August, September, 1848). *The Song of King Canute* was transferred from *Miss Tickletoby's Lectures on English History* in *Punch* to *Rebecca and Rowena*. The burlesque was not illustrated in *Fraser's Magazine*, and the illustrations were drawn by Richard Doyle for the issue in book-form. The original title-page ran : Rebecca | and Rowena. | A | Romance upon Romance. | By Mr. M. A. Titmarsh. | With illustrations by Richard Doyle. | London : | Chapman and Hall, 186 Strand. | 1850.

Punch's Prize Novelists appeared in *Punch* from April to October 1847. *George de Barnwell, Codlingsby, Lords and Liveries, Barbazure*, and *Phil Fogarty* were reprinted in *Punch's Prize Novelists, The Fat Contributor*, and *Travels in London* (Appleton's Popular Library of the Best Authors, New York, 1853) ; and also, under the title of *Novels by Eminent Hands*, in *Miscellanies* (vol. 2 ; London, 1856). *Crinoline* and *Stars and Stripes* were first reprinted in the Library edition of the Collected

Works (vol. 16, 1869). *A Plan for a Prize Novel*, which, strictly speaking, is not one of the *Novels by Eminent Hands*, was also first printed in *Punch*—on February 22, 1851. This was reprinted in a supplementary volume of the Library edition of the Collected Works (vol. 24, 1886).

Notes of a Journey from Cornhill to Grand Cairo was published in 1846, and contained a coloured frontispiece and several illustrations by the Author. The original title-page ran : Notes of a Journey | From | Cornhill to | Grand Cairo, | by way of | Lisbon, Athens, Constantinople, | and Jerusalem : | Performed in the Steamers of the Peninsular and | Oriental Company. | By Mr. M. A. Titmarsh, | Author of ' The Irish Sketch Book,' etc. | London : | Chapman and Hall, 186 Strand. | MDCCCXLVI.

Under the heading of *Juvenilia* are included the writings of Thackeray before he became a professional man of letters. He was not a precocious lad, but he began to write and draw at an early age. While at the Charterhouse he parodied Miss Landon's hyper-sentimental poem ' Violets ' in a style which shows clearly that even then he had the sense of humour and the eye for the ridiculous which distinguished his later work.

VIOLETS (L. E. L.).	CABBAGES (W. M. T.).
Violets ! deep blue violets !	Cabbages ! bright green cabbages !
April's loveliest coronets :	April's loveliest gifts, I guess.
There are no flowers grow in the vale,	There is not a plant in the garden laid,
Kissed by the sun, woo'd by the gale,	Raised by the dung, dug by the spade,
None with the dew of the twilight wet,	None by the gardener watered, I ween,
So sweet as the deep blue violet.	So sweet as the cabbage, the cabbage green.
I do remember how sweet a breath	I do remember how sweet a smell
Came with the azure light of a wreath,	Came with the cabbage I loved so well,
That hung round the wild harp's golden chords	Served up with the best that beautiful looked,
That rang to my dark-eyed lover's words.	The beef that dark-eyed Ellen cooked.

I have seen that dear harp rolled
With gems of the East and bands of gold,
But it never was sweeter than when set
With leaves of the dark blue violet.

And when the grave shall open for me—
I care not how soon that time may be—
Never a rose shall bloom on my tomb,
It breathes too much of hope and bloom ;
But let me have there the meek regret
Of the bending and deep blue violet.

I have seen beef served with radish of horse,
I have seen beef served with lettuce of cos,
But it is far nicer, far nicer, I guess,
As bubble and squeak, beef and cabbages.

And when the dinner-bell sounds for me—
I care not how soon that time may be—
Carrots shall never be served on my cloth,
They are far too sweet for a boy of my broth ;
But let me have there a mighty mess
Of smoking hot beef and cabbages.

Probably about this time he also wrote some lines of doggerel which show his tendency to indulge in almost impossible rhymes that was always a distinguishing feature of his humorous poetry. These begin : 'In the romantic little town of Highbury'; and were reprinted by Anthony Trollope in the monograph on Thackeray in the 'English Men of Letters' series. Another early effort was a *Holyday Song*, printed in full in *The Grey-Friar* by Mr. Davies, of which a few verses may be here reproduced.

> Now let us dance and sing,
> While Carthusian bells do ring ;
> Joy twangs the fiddle-string,
>   And Freedom blows the flute.

> Tiddle-dum and Tiddle-di—
> What a joke for you and I—
> Dulce domum, let us cry—
>   Charterhouse adieu.

> Purblind Cupid still drag on
> Some more days ere he can brag on
> Killing game to fill a waggon,
>   And thy shooting-jacket too !

> Yet, oh stay ! thou beauteous sister
> Who has caused heartburn and blister
> To that paragon young mister,
>   Joseph Carne !
>
> Queen of Beauty ! Star of Harrow !
> Thou has shot thro' heart and marrow
> And stricken Makepeace with thy arrow
>   In the head-brain.

At Cambridge he contributed to a little weekly paper, called *The Snob : a Literary and Scientific Journal NOT 'Conducted by Members of the University.'* The first number appeared on April 9, 1829 ; and the eleventh and last bears the date of June 18. This was continued after the long vacation under the title of *The Gownsman.* It is believed that he edited the seventeen numbers, which came out between November 5, 1829, and February 25, 1830 ; but only a few of his contributions have been identified. While still up at Trinity College he wrote a parody of a speech of Lalor Sheil upon Penenden Heath, which he was not allowed to deliver, but of which, before he left town, he took the precaution to send copies to the leading journals for insertion. This *jeu d'esprit* was printed in *The Western Luminary,* and is here inserted rather because it was his first appearance in the public prints than because of its merits.

IRISH MELODY

(Air : *The Minstrel Boy*)

> Mister Sheil into Kent has gone
>   On Penenden Heath you'll find him ;
> Nor think you that he came alone,
>   There's Doctor Doyle behind him.
>
> ' Men of Kent,' said the little man,
>   ' If you hate Emancipation,
> You're a set of fools.' He then began
>   A cut and dry oration.
>
> He strove to speak, but the men of Kent
>   Began a grievous shouting,
> When out of the waggon the little man went,
>   And put a stop to his spouting.

REBECCA AND

AND

ROWENA.

A

ROMANCE UPON ROMANCE.

BY

Mr MICHAEL ANGELO TITMARSH.

ILLUSTRATED BY RICHARD DOYLE.

LONDON:
CHAPMAN AND HALL, 186, STRAND.
1850.

Price 5s. plain, or 7s. 6d. coloured.

REDUCED FACSIMILE OF THE ORIGINAL COVER

'What though these heretics heard me not!'
Quoth he to his friend Canonical,
'My speech is safe in the *Times*, I wot,
And eke in the *Morning Chronicle*.'

On January 5, 1833, F. W. N. Bayley brought out *The National Standard and Journal of Literature, Science, Music, Theatricals, and the Fine Arts*. Thackeray soon became a contributor, and with the nineteenth number took over the editorship, which change he announced in the first *Address*, on May 11. Some weeks later he bought the paper. The last number of the year contained a second *Address*, in which the future success of the journal is spoken of as assured. The next issue bore a fresh title: *The National Standard and Literary Representative*; but, in spite of the editor's confidence, the paper issued its last number on February 1, 1834. It is generally—and, there is reason to believe, correctly—believed that Thackeray related the tale of this venture in the pages of *Lovel the Widower*.

None of the drawings or articles—with the exception of the burlesque poem *Timbuctoo*—printed under the heading of *Juvenilia* have ever before been included in any complete edition of Thackeray's works.

L. M.

CONTENTS

BURLESQUES

A LEGEND OF THE RHINE

CHAPTER VII

CHAPTER VIII

CHAPTER IX

CHAPTER X

CHAPTER XI

CHAPTER XII

CHAPTER XIII

REBECCA AND ROWENA

CHAPTER I

CHAPTER II

CHAPTER III

CHAPTER IV

CHAPTER V

CHAPTER VI

CHAPTER VII

NOVELS BY EMINENT HANDS

FROM CORNHILL TO GRAND CAIRO

BURLESQUES

A LEGEND OF THE RHINE

A LEGEND OF THE RHINE

CHAPTER I

SIR LUDWIG OF HOMBOURG

IT WAS in the good old days of chivalry, when every mountain that bathes its shadow in the Rhine had its castle: not inhabited, as now, by a few rats and owls, nor covered with moss and wall-flowers, and funguses, and creeping ivy. No, no! where the ivy now clusters there grew strong portcullis and bars of steel; where the wall-flower now quivers on the rampart there were silken banners embroidered with wonderful heraldry; men-at-arms marched where now you shall only see a bank of moss or a hideous black champignon; and in place of the rats and owlets, I warrant me there were ladies and knights to revel in the great halls, and to feast, and to dance, and to make love there. They are passed away:—those old knights and ladies: their golden hair first changed to silver, and then the silver dropped off and disappeared for ever; their elegant legs, so slim and active in the dance, became swollen and gouty, and then, from being swollen and gouty, dwindled down to bare bone-shanks; the roses left their cheeks, and then their cheeks disappeared, and left their skulls, and then their skulls powdered into dust, and all sign of them

3

was gone. And as it was with them, so shall it be with us. Ho, seneschal! fill me a cup of liquor! put sugar in it, good fellow— yea, and a little hot water; a very little, for my soul is sad, as I think of those days and knights of old.

They, too, have revelled and feasted, and where are they?— gone?—nay, not altogether gone; for doth not the eye catch glimpses of them as they walk yonder in the grey limbo of romance, shining faintly in their coats of steel, wandering by the side of long-haired ladies, with long-tailed gowns that little pages carry? Yes! one sees them: the poet sees them still in the far-off Cloudland, and hears the ring of their clarions as they hasten to battle or tourney—and the dim echoes of their lutes chanting of love and fair ladies! Gracious privilege of poesy! It is as the Dervish's collyrium to the eyes, and causes them to see treasures that to the sight of donkeys are invisible. Blessed treasures of fancy! I would not change ye—no, not for many donkey-loads of gold. . . . Fill again, jolly seneschal, thou brave wag; chalk me up the produce on the hostel door—surely the spirits of old are mixed up in the wondrous liquor, and gentle visions of bygone princes and princesses look blandly down on us from the cloudy perfume of the pipe. Do you know in what year the fairies left the Rhine?—long before Murray's 'Guide-Book' was wrote—long before squat steamboats, with snorting funnels, came paddling down the stream. Do you not know that once upon a time the appearance of eleven thousand British virgins was considered at Cologne as a wonder? Now there come twenty thousand such annually, accompanied by their ladies'-maids. But of them we will say no more—let us back to those who went before them.

Many many hundred thousand years ago, and at the exact period when chivalry was in full bloom, there occurred a little history upon the banks of the Rhine, which has been already written in a book, and hence must be positively true. 'Tis a story of knights and ladies—of love and battle, and virtue rewarded; a story of princes and noble lords, moreover: the best of company. Gentles, an ye will, ye shall hear it. Fair dames and damsels, may your loves be as happy as those of the heroine of this romaunt.

On the cold and rainy evening of Thursday, the 26th of October, in the year previously indicated, such travellers as might have chanced to be abroad in that bitter night, might have remarked a fellow-wayfarer journeying on the road from Oberwinter to Godesberg. He was a man not tall in stature, but of the most athletic proportions, and Time, which had browned and furrowed his cheek and sprinkled his locks with grey, declared pretty clearly that He must have been acquainted with the warrior for some fifty good years. He was armed in mail, and rode a powerful and active battle-horse, which (though the way the pair had come that day was long and weary indeed) yet supported the warrior, his armour and luggage, with seeming ease. As it was in a friend's country, the knight did not think fit to wear his heavy *destrier*, or helmet, which hung at his saddle-bow over his portmanteau. Both were marked with the coronet of a count; and from the crown which

surmounted the helmet, rose the crest of his knightly race, an arm proper lifting a naked sword.

At his right hand, and convenient to the warrior's grasp, hung his mangonel or mace—a terrific weapon which had shattered the brains of many a turbaned soldan: while over his broad and ample chest there fell the triangular shield of the period, whereon were emblazoned his arms—argent, a gules wavy, on a saltire reversed of the second: the latter device was awarded for a daring exploit before Ascalon, by the Emperor Maximilian, and a reference to the German Peerage of that day, or a knowledge of high families which every gentleman then possessed, would have sufficed to show at once that the rider we have described was of the noble house of Hombourg. It was, in fact, the gallant knight Sir Ludwig of Hombourg: his rank as a count, and chamberlain of the Emperor of Austria, was marked by the cap of maintenance with the peacock's feather which he wore (when not armed for battle), and his princely blood was denoted by the oiled silk umbrella which he carried (a very meet protection against the pitiless storm), and which, as it is known, in the Middle Ages, none but princes were justified in using. A bag, fastened with a brazen padlock, and made of the costly produce of the Persian looms (then extremely rare in Europe), told that he had travelled in Eastern climes. This, too, was evident from the inscription writ on card or parchment, and sewed on the bag. It first ran, 'Count Ludwig de Hombourg, Jerusalem'; but the name of the Holy City had been dashed out with the pen, and that of 'Godesberg' substituted. So far indeed had the cavalier travelled!—and it is needless to state that the bag in question contained such remaining articles of the toilet as the high-born noble deemed unnecessary to place in his valise.

'By Saint Bugo of Katzenellenbogen!' said the good knight, shivering, ''tis colder here than at Damascus! Marry, I am so hungry I could eat one of Saladin's camels. Shall I be at Godesberg in time for dinner?' And taking out his horologe (which hung in a small side-pocket of his embroidered surcoat), the crusader consoled himself by finding that it was but seven of the night, and that he would reach Godesberg ere the warder had sounded the second gong.

His opinion was borne out by the result. His good steed, which could trot at a pinch fourteen leagues in the hour, brought him to this famous castle, just as the warder was giving the first welcome signal which told that the princely family of Count Karl, Margrave of Godesberg, were about to prepare for their usual repast at eight o'clock. Crowds of pages and horsekeepers were in the court, when, the portcullis being raised, and amidst the respectful salutes of the sentinels, the most ancient friend of the house of Godesberg entered into its castle-yard. The under-butler stepped forward to take his bridle-rein. 'Welcome, Sir Count, from the Holy Land!' exclaimed the faithful old man. 'Welcome, Sir Count, from the Holy Land!' cried the rest of the servants in the hall. A stable was speedily found for the Count's horse, Streithengst, and it was not before the gallant soldier had seen that true animal well cared for, that he entered the castle itself, and was conducted to his chamber. Wax candles burning bright on the mantel, flowers in china vases, every variety of soap, and a flask of the precious essence manufactured at the neighbouring city of Cologne, were displayed on his toilet table; a cheering fire 'crackled on the hearth,' and showed that the good knight's coming had been looked and cared for. The serving-maidens, bringing him hot water for his ablutions, smiling asked, 'Would he have his couch warmed at eve?' One might have been sure from their blushes that the tough old soldier made an arch reply. The family tonsor came to know whether the noble Count had need of his skill. 'By Saint Bugo,' said the knight, as seated in an easy settle by the fire, the tonsor rid his chin of its stubbly growth, and lightly passed the tongs and pomatum through 'the

sable silver' of his hair,—'By Saint Bugo, this is better than my dungeon at Grand Cairo. How is my godson Otto, master barber; and the Lady Countess, his mother; and the noble Count Karl, my dear brother-in-arms?'

'They are well,' said the tonsor, with a sigh.

'By Saint Bugo, I'm glad on't; but why that sigh?'

'Things are not as they have been with my good lord,' answered the hairdresser, 'ever since Count Gottfried's arrival.'

'He here!' roared Sir Ludwig. 'Good never came where Gottfried was!' and the while he donned a pair of silken hose, that showed admirably the proportions of his lower limbs, and exchanged his coat of mail for the spotless vest and black surcoat collared with velvet of Genoa, which was the fitting costume for ' knight in ladye's bower,'—the knight entered into a conversation with the barber, who explained to him, with the usual garrulousness of his tribe, what was the present position of the noble family of Godesberg.

This will be narrated in the next chapter.

CHAPTER II

'TIS needless to state that the gallant warrior Ludwig of Hombourg found in the bosom of his friend's family a cordial welcome. The brother-in-arms of the Margrave Karl, he was the esteemed friend of the Margravine, the exalted and beautiful Theodora of Boppum, and (albeit no theologian, and although the first princes of Christendom coveted such an honour) he was selected to stand as sponsor for the Margrave's son Otto, the only child of his house.

It was now seventeen years since the Count and Countess had been united : and although Heaven had not blessed their couch with more than one child, it may be said of that one that it was a prize, and that surely never lighted on the earth a more delightful vision. When Count Ludwig, hastening to the holy wars, had quitted his beloved godchild, he had left him a boy ; he now found him, as the latter rushed into his arms, grown to be one of the finest young men in Germany : tall and excessively graceful in proportion, with the blush of health mantling upon his cheek, that was likewise adorned with the first down of manhood, and with magnificent golden ringlets, such as a Rowland might envy, curling over his brow and his shoulders.   His eyes alternately beamed with the fire of daring, or melted with the moist glance of benevolence.   Well might a mother be proud of such a boy.   Well might the brave Ludwig exclaim, as he clasped the youth to his breast, ' By Saint Bugo of Katzenellenbogen, Otto, thou art fit to be one of Cœur de Lion's grenadiers ! ' and it was the fact : the ' Childe' of Godesberg measured six feet three.

He was habited for the evening meal in the costly though simple attire of the nobleman of the period—and his costume a good deal resembled that of the old knight whose toilet we have just described ; with the difference of colour, however.   The *pourpoint* worn by young Otto of Godesberg was of blue, handsomely decorated with buttons of carved and embossed gold ; his *haut-de-chausses*, or leggings, were of the stuff of Nanquin, then brought

9

by the Lombard argosies at an immense price from China. The neighbouring country of Holland had supplied his wrists and bosom with the most costly laces; and thus attired, with an opera-hat placed on one side of his head, ornamented with a single flower (that brilliant one, the tulip), the boy rushed into his godfather's dressing-room, and warned him that the banquet was ready.

It was indeed: a frown had gathered on the dark brows of the Lady Theodora, and her bosom heaved with an emotion akin to indignation; for she feared lest the soups in the refectory and the splendid fish now smoking there were getting cold: she feared not for herself, but for her lord's sake. 'Godesberg,' whispered she to Count Ludwig, as trembling on his arm they descended from the drawing-room, 'Godesberg is sadly changed of late.'

'By Saint Bugo!' said the burly knight, starting, 'these are the very words the barber spake.'

The lady heaved a sigh, and placed herself before the soup-tureen. For some time the good Knight Ludwig of Hombourg was too much occupied in ladling out the forcemeat balls and rich calves' head of which the delicious pottage was formed (in ladling them out, did we say? ay, marry, and in eating them, too) to look at his brother-in-arms at the bottom of the table, where he sat with his son on his left hand, and the Baron Gottfried on his right.

The Margrave was *indeed* changed. 'By Saint Bugo,' whispered Ludwig to the Countess, 'your husband is as surly as a bear that hath been wounded o' the head.' Tears falling into her soup-plate were her only reply. The soup, the turbot, the haunch of mutton, Count Ludwig remarked that the Margrave sent all away untasted.

'The boteler will serve ye with wine, Hombourg,' said the Margrave gloomily from the end of the table. Not even an invitation to drink: how different was this from the old times!

But when, in compliance with this order, the boteler proceeded to hand round the mantling vintage of the Cape to the assembled party, and to fill young Otto's goblet (which the latter held up with the eagerness of youth), the Margrave's rage knew no bounds. He rushed at his son; he dashed the wine-cup over his spotless vest; and giving him three or four heavy blows which would have knocked down a bonasus, but only caused the young Childe to blush: '*You* take wine!' roared out the Margrave; '*you* dare to help yourself! Who the d–v–l gave *you* leave to help yourself?' and the terrible blows were reiterated over the delicate ears of the boy.

'Ludwig! Ludwig!' shrieked the Margravine.

'Hold your prate, madam,' roared the Prince. 'By Saint Buffo, mayn't a father beat his own child?'

'HIS OWN CHILD!' repeated the Margrave with a burst, almost a shriek, of indescribable agony. 'Ah, what did I say?'

Sir Ludwig looked about him in amaze; Sir Gottfried (at the Margrave's right hand) smiled ghastlily; the young Otto was too much agitated by the recent conflict to wear any expression but that of extreme discomfiture; but the poor Margravine turned her head aside and blushed, red almost as the lobster which flanked the turbot before her.

In those rude old times, 'tis known such table quarrels were by no means unusual amongst gallant knights; and Ludwig, who had oft seen the Margrave cast a leg of mutton at an offending servitor, or empty a sauce-boat in the direction of the Margravine, thought this was but one of the usual outbreaks of his worthy though irascible friend, and wisely determined to change the converse.

'How is my friend,' said he, 'the good knight, Sir Hildebrandt?'

'By Saint Buffo, this is too much!' screamed the Margrave, and actually rushed from the room.

'By Saint Bugo,' said his friend, 'gallant knights, gentle sirs, what ails my good Lord Margrave?'

'Perhaps his nose bleeds,' said Gottfried with a sneer.

'Ah, my kind friend,' said the Margravine with uncontrollable emotion, 'I fear some of you have passed from the frying-pan into the fire.' And making the signal of departure to the ladies, they rose and retired to coffee in the drawing-room.

The Margrave presently came back again, somewhat more collected than he had been. 'Otto,' he said sternly, 'go join the ladies: it becomes not a young boy to remain in the company of gallant knights after dinner.' The noble Childe with manifest unwillingness quitted the room, and the Margrave, taking his lady's place at the head of the table, whispered to Sir Ludwig, 'Hildebrandt will be here to-night to an evening party, given in honour of your return from Palestine. My good friend—my true friend—my old companion in arms, Sir Gottfried! you had best see that the fiddlers be not drunk, and that the crumpets be gotten ready.' Sir Gottfried, obsequiously taking his patron's hint, bowed and left the room.

'You shall know all soon, dear Ludwig,' said the Margrave with a heartrending look. 'You marked Gottfried, who left the room anon?'

'I did.'

'You look incredulous concerning his worth; but I tell thee, Ludwig, that yonder Gottfried is a good fellow, and my fast friend. Why should he not be? He is my near relation heir to my

property : should I ' (here the Margrave's countenance assumed its
former expression of excruciating agony),—' *should I have no son.*'

' But I never saw the boy in better health,' replied Sir Ludwig.

' Nevertheless,—ha ! ha !—it may chance that I shall soon
have no son.'

The Margrave had crushed many a cup of wine during dinner,
and Sir Ludwig thought naturally that his gallant friend had
drunken rather deeply.   He proceeded in this respect to imitate
him ; for the stern soldier of those days neither shrunk before the
Paynim nor the punch-bowl : and many a rousing night had our
crusader enjoyed in Syria with lion-hearted Richard ; with his
coadjutor, Godfrey of Bouillon ; nay, with the dauntless Saladin
himself.

' You knew Gottfried in Palestine ?' asked the Marquis.

' I did.'

' Why did ye not greet him then, as ancient comrades should,
with the warm grasp of friendship ?   It is not because Sir Gottfried is poor ?   You know well that he is of race as noble as thine
own, my early friend ! '

' I care not for his race nor for his poverty,' replied the blunt
crusader.   ' What says the Minnesinger ?   " Marry, the rank is
but the stamp of the guinea ; the man is the gold."   And I tell
thee, Karl of Godesberg, that yonder Gottfried is base metal.'

' By Saint Buffo, thou beliest him, dear Ludwig.'

' By Saint Bugo, dear Karl, I say sooth.   The fellow was
known i' the camp of the crusaders—disreputably known.   Ere
he joined us in Palestine, he had sojourned in Constantinople, and
learned the arts of the Greek.   He is a cogger of dice, I tell thee—
a chanter of horseflesh.   He won five thousand marks from bluff
Richard of England the night before the storming of Ascalon, and
I caught him with false trumps in his pocket.   He warranted a
bay mare to Conrad of Mont Serrat, and the rogue had fired her.'

' Ha ! mean ye that Sir Gottfried is a *leg ?* ' cried Sir Karl,
knitting his brows.   ' Now, by my blessed patron, Saint Buffo of
Bonn, had any other but Ludwig of Hombourg so said, I would
have cloven him from skull to chine.'

' By Saint Bugo of Katzenellenbogen, I will prove my words on
Sir Gottfried's body—not on thine, old brother-in-arms.   And to
do the knave justice, he is a good lance.   Holy Bugo ! but he did
good service at Acre !   But his character was such that, spite of
his bravery, he was dismissed the army ; nor even allowed to sell
his captain's commission.'

' I have heard of it,' said the Margrave ; ' Gottfried hath told
me of it.   'Twas about some silly quarrel over the wine-cup—a

mere silly jape, believe me. Hugo de Brodenel would have no
black bottle on the board. Gottfried was wroth, and, to say sooth,
flung the black bottle at the Count's head. Hence his dismission
and abrupt return. But you know not,' continued the Margrave,
with a heavy sigh, ' of what use that worthy Gottfried has been
to me. He has uncloaked a traitor to me.'

' Not *yet*,' answered Hombourg satirically.

' By Saint Buffo ! a deep-dyed dastard ! a dangerous damnable
traitor !—a nest of traitors. Hildebrandt is a traitor—Otto is a
traitor—and Theodora (O Heaven !) she—she is *another*.' The
old Prince burst into tears at the word, and was almost choked
with emotion.

' What means this passion, dear friend ?' cried Sir Ludwig,
seriously alarmed.

' Mark, Ludwig ! mark Hildebrandt and Theodora together :
mark Hildebrandt and *Otto* together. Like, like I tell thee as
two peas. O holy saints, that I should be born to suffer this !—
to have all my affections wrenched out of my bosom, and to be
left alone in my old age ! But, hark ! the guests are arriving.
An ye will not empty another flask of claret, let us join the ladyes
i' the withdrawing chamber. When there, mark *Hildebrandt and
Otto !*'

CHAPTER III

HE festival was indeed begun. Coming on horseback, or in their caroches, knights and ladies of the highest rank were assembled in the grand saloon of Godesberg, which was splendidly illuminated to receive them. Servitors, in rich liveries (they were attired in doublets of the sky-blue broadcloth of Ypres, and hose of the richest yellow sammit— the colours of the house of Godesberg), bore about various refreshments on trays of silver — cakes, baked in the oven, and swimming in melted butter; munchets of bread, smeared with the same delicious condiment, and carved so thin that you might have expected them to take wing and fly to the ceiling; coffee, introduced by Peter the Hermit, after his excursion into Arabia, and tea such as only Bohemia could produce, circulated amidst the festive throng, and were eagerly devoured by the guests. The Margrave's gloom was unheeded by them—how little indeed is the smiling crowd aware of the pangs that are lurking in the breasts of those who bid them to the feast! The Margravine was pale; but woman knows how to deceive; she was more than ordinarily courteous to her friends, and laughed, though the laugh was hollow; and talked, though the talk was loathsome to her.

'The two are together,' said the Margrave, clutching his friend's shoulder. *'Now look!'*

Sir Ludwig turned towards a quadrille, and there, sure enough, were Sir Hildebrandt and young Otto standing side by side in the

dance.   Two eggs were not more like!   The reason of the
Margrave's horrid suspicion at once flashed across his friend's
mind

''Tis clear as the staff of a pike,' said the poor Margrave
mournfully.   'Come, brother, away from the scene; let us go
play a game at cribbage!' and retiring to the Margravine's *boudoir*,
the two warriors sat down to the game.

But though 'tis an interesting one, and though the Margrave

won, yet he could not keep his attention on the cards : so agitated
was his mind by the dreadful secret which weighed upon it.   In
the midst of their play, the obsequious Gottfried came to whisper
a word in his patron's ear, which threw the latter into such a
fury, that apoplexy was apprehended by the two lookers-on.   But
the Margrave mastered his emotion.   '*At what time*, did you
say?' said he to Gottfried.

'At daybreak, at the outer gate.'

'I will be there.'

'*And so will I too*,' thought Count Ludwig, the good Knight
of Hombourg.

CHAPTER IV

THE FLIGHT

How often does man, proud man, make calculations for the future, and think he can bend stern fate to his will! Alas, we are but creatures in its hands! How many a slip between the lip and the lifted wine-cup! How often, though seemingly with a choice of couches to repose upon, do we find ourselves dashed to earth; and then we are fain to say the grapes are sour, because we cannot attain them; or worse, to yield to anger in consequence of our own fault. Sir Ludwig, the Hombourger, was *not at the outer gate* at daybreak.

He slept until ten of the clock. The previous night's potations had been heavy, the day's journey had been long and rough. The knight slept as a soldier would, to whom a feather bed is a rarity, and who wakes not till he hears the blast of the réveillé.

He looked up as he woke. At his bedside sat the Margrave. He had been there for hours, watching his slumbering comrade. Watching?—no, not watching, but awake by his side, brooding over thoughts unutterably bitter—over feelings inexpressibly wretched.

'What's o'clock?' was the first natural exclamation of the Hombourger.

'I believe it is five o'clock,' said his friend. It was ten. It might have been twelve, two, half-past four, twenty minutes to six, the Margrave would still have said, ' *I believe it is five o'clock.*' The wretched take no count of time: it flies with unequal pinions, indeed, for *them*.

'Is breakfast over?' inquired the crusader.

'Ask the butler,' said the Margrave, nodding his head wildly, rolling his eyes wildly, smiling wildly.

'Gracious Bugo!' said the Knight of Hombourg, 'what has ailed thee, my friend? It is ten o'clock by my horologe. Your regular hour is nine. You are not—no, by heavens! you are not shaved! You wear the tights and silken hose of last evening's banquet. Your collar is all rumpled—'tis that of yesterday. *You have not been to bed!* What has chanced, brother of mine; what has chanced?'

16

'A common chance, Louis of Hombourg,' said the Margrave: 'one that chances every day. A false woman, a false friend, a broken heart. *This* has chanced. I have not been to bed.'

'What mean ye?' cried Count Ludwig, deeply affected. 'A false friend? *I* am not a false friend. A false woman? Surely the lovely Theodora, your wife——'

'I have no wife, Louis, now; I have no wife and no son.'

In accents broken by grief, the Margrave explained what had occurred. Gottfried's information was but too correct. There was *a cause* for the likeness between Otto and Sir Hildebrandt: a fatal cause! Hildebrandt and Theodora had met at dawn at the outer gate. The Margrave had seen them. They walked along together; they embraced. Ah! how the husband's, the father's, feelings were harrowed at that embrace! They parted; and then the Margrave, coming forward, coldly signified to his lady that she was to retire to a convent for life, and gave orders that the boy should be sent too, to take the vows at a monastery.

Both sentences had been executed. Otto, in a boat, and guarded by a company of his father's men-at-arms, was on the river going towards Cologne, to the Monastery of Saint Buffo there. The Lady Theodora, under the guard of Sir Gottfried and an attendant, were on their way to the convent of Nonnenwerth, which many of our readers have seen— the beautiful Green Island Convent, laved by the bright waters of the Rhine!

'What road did Gottfried take?' asked the Knight of Hombourg, grinding his teeth.

'You cannot overtake him,' said the Margrave. 'My good Gottfried, he is my only comfort now: he is my kinsman, and shall be my heir. He will be back anon.'

'Will he so?' thought Sir Ludwig. 'I will ask him a few questions ere he return.' And springing from his couch, he began forthwith to put on his usual morning dress of complete armour; and, after a hasty ablution, donned, not his cap of maintenance, but his helmet of battle. He rang the bell violently.

'A cup of coffee, straight,' said he, to the servitor who answered the summons; 'bid the cook pack me a sausage and bread in paper, and the groom saddle Streithengst: we have far to ride.'

The various orders were obeyed. The horse was brought; the refreshments disposed of; the clattering steps of the departing steed were heard in the courtyard; but the Margrave took no notice of his friend, and sat, plunged in silent grief, quite motionless by the empty bedside.

CHAPTER V

THE Hombourger led his horse down the winding path which conducts from the hill and castle of Godesberg into the beautiful green plain below. Who has not seen that lovely plain, and who that has seen it has not loved it? A thousand sunny vineyards and cornfields stretch around in peaceful luxuriance; the mighty Rhine floats by it in silver magnificence, and on the opposite bank rise the seven mountains robed in majestic purple, the monarchs of the royal scene.

A pleasing poet, Lord Byron, in describing this very scene, has mentioned that ' peasant girls, with dark blue eyes, and hands that offer cake and wine,' are perpetually crowding round the traveller in this delicious district, and proffering to him their rustic presents. This was no doubt the case in former days, when the noble bard wrote his elegant poems—in the happy ancient days! when maidens were as yet generous, and men kindly! Now the degenerate peasantry of the district are much more inclined to ask than to give, and their blue eyes seem to have disappeared with their generosity.

But as it was a long time ago that the events of our story occurred, 'tis probable that the good Knight Ludwig of Hombourg was greeted upon his path by this fascinating peasantry; though we know not how he accepted their welcome. He continued his ride across the flat green country until he came to Rolandseck, whence he could command the Island of Nonnenwerth (that lies in the Rhine opposite that place), and all who went to it or passed from it.

Over the entrance of a little cavern in one of the rocks hanging above the Rhine-stream at Rolandseck, and covered with odoriferous cactuses and silvery magnolias, the traveller of the present day may perceive a rude broken image of a saint: that image represented the venerable Saint Buffo of Bonn, the patron of the Margrave; and Sir Ludwig, kneeling on the greensward, and reciting a censer, an ave, and a couple of acolytes before it, felt encouraged to think that the deed he meditated was about to be performed under the very eyes of his friend's sanctified patron.   His devotion done (and the knight of those days was as pious as he was brave), Sir Ludwig, the gallant Hombourger, exclaimed with a loud voice :—

'Ho! hermit! holy hermit, art thou in thy cell!'

'Who calls the poor servant of Heaven and Saint Buffo?' exclaimed a voice from the cavern ; and presently, from beneath the wreaths of geranium and magnolia, appeared an intensely venerable, ancient, and majestic head—'twas that, we need not say, of Saint Buffo's solitary.   A silver beard hanging to his knees gave his person an appearance of great respectability ; his body was robed in simple brown serge, and girt with a knotted cord ; his ancient feet were only defended from the prickles and stones by the rudest sandals, and his bald and polished head was bare.

'Holy hermit,' said the knight in a grave voice, 'make ready thy ministry, for there is some one about to die.'

'Where, son?'

'Here, father.'

'Is he here, now?'

'Perhaps,' said the stout warrior, crossing himself ; 'but not so if right prevail.'   At this moment he caught sight of a ferry-boat putting off from Nonnenwerth, with a knight on board.   Ludwig knew at once, by the sinople reversed and the truncated gules on his surcoat, that it was Sir Gottfried of Godesberg.

'Be ready, father,' said the good knight, pointing towards the advancing boat ; and waving his hand by way of respect to the reverend hermit, without a further word he vaulted into his saddle, and rode back for a few score of paces, when he wheeled round, and remained steady.   His great lance and pennon rose in the air.   His armour glistened in the sun ; the chest and head of his battle-horse were similarly covered with steel.   As Sir Gottfried, likewise armed and mounted (for his horse had been left at the ferry hard by), advanced up the road, he almost started at the figure before him— a glistening tower of steel.

'Are you the lord of this pass, Sir Knight?' said Sir Gottfried haughtily, 'or do you hold it against all comers, in honour of your lady-love?'

'I am not the lord of this pass.   I do not hold it against all comers.   I hold it but against one, and he is a liar and a traitor.'

'As the matter concerns me not, I pray you let me pass,' said Gottfried.

'The matter *does* concern thee, Gottfried of Godesberg.   Liar and traitor! art thou coward, too?'

'Holy Saint Buffo! 'tis a fight!' exclaimed the old hermit (who, too, had been a gallant warrior in his day) ; and like the old war-horse that hears the trumpet's sound, and spite of his clerical profession, he prepared to look on at the combat with no ordinary eagerness, and sat down on the overhanging ledge of the rock, lighting his pipe, and affecting unconcern, but in reality most deeply interested in the event which was about to ensue.

As soon as the word 'coward' had been pronounced by Sir Ludwig, his opponent, uttering a curse far too horrible to be inscribed here, had wheeled back his powerful piebald, and brought his lance to the rest.

'Ha! Beauséant!' cried he. 'Allah humdillah!' 'Twas the battle-cry in Palestine of the irresistible Knights Hospitallers. 'Look to thyself, Sir Knight, and for mercy from Heaven. *I* will give thee none.'

'A Bugo for Katzenellenbogen!' exclaimed Sir Ludwig piously : that, too, was the well-known war-cry of his princely race.

'I will give the signal,' said the old hermit, waving his pipe. 'Knights, are you ready? One, two, three. *Los!*' (Let go.)

At the signal, the two steeds tore up the ground like whirl-winds ; the two knights, two flashing perpendicular masses of steel, rapidly converged ; the two lances met upon the two shields of either, and shivered, splintered, shattered into ten hundred thousand pieces, which whirled through the air here and there, among the rocks, or in the trees, or in the river. The two horses fell back trembling on their haunches, where they remained for half a minute or so.

'Holy Buffo! a brave stroke!' said the old hermit. 'Marry, but a splinter well-nigh took off my nose!' The honest hermit waved his pipe in delight, not perceiving that one of the splinters had carried off the head of it, and rendered his favourite amusement impossible. 'Ha! they are to it again! O my! how they go to with their great swords! Well stricken, grey! Well parried, piebald! Ha, that was a slicer! Go it, piebald! go it, grey!—go it, grey! go it, pie—— Peccavi! peccavi!' said the old man, here suddenly closing his eyes, and falling down on his knees. 'I forgot I was a man of peace.' And the next moment, uttering a hasty matin, he sprang down the ledge of rock, and was by the side of the combatants.

The battle was over. Good knight as Sir Gottfried was, his strength and skill had not been able to overcome Sir Ludwig the Hombourger, with RIGHT on his side. He was bleeding at every point of his armour : he had been run through the body several times, and a cut in tierce, delivered with tremendous dexterity, had

cloven the crown of his helmet of Damascus steel, and passing
through the cerebellum and sensorium, had split his nose almost
in twain.

His mouth foaming—his face almost green—his eyes full of

GC.

blood—his brains spattered over his forehead, and several of his
teeth knocked out—the discomfited warrior presented a ghastly
spectacle, as, reeling under the effects of the last tremendous blow
which the Knight of Hombourg dealt, Sir Gottfried fell heavily
from the saddle of his piebald charger; the frightened animal
whisked his tail wildly with a shriek and a snort, plunged out his

hind legs, trampling for one moment upon the feet of the prostrate Gottfried, thereby causing him to shriek with agony, and then galloped away riderless.

Away ! ay, away !—away amid the green vineyards and golden cornfields ; away up the steep mountains, where he frightened the eagles in their eyries ; away down the clattering ravines, where the flashing cataracts tumble ; away through the dark pine-forests, where the hungry wolves are howling ; away over the dreary wolds, where the wild wind walks alone ; away through the plashing quagmires, where the will-o'-the-wisp slunk frightened among the reeds ; away through light and darkness, storm and sunshine ; away by tower and town, highroad and hamlet.   Once a turnpike-man would have detained him ; but, ha ! ha ! he charged the pike, and cleared it at a bound.   Once the Cologne Diligence stopped the way : he charged the Diligence, he knocked off the cap of the conductor on the roof, and yet galloped wildly, madly, furiously, irresistibly on !   Brave horse ! gallant steed ! snorting child of Araby !   On went the horse, over mountains, rivers, turnpikes, apple-women ; and never stopped until he reached a livery-stable in Cologne where his master was accustomed to put him up.

CHAPTER VI

THE CONFESSION

But we have forgotten, meanwhile, the prostrate individual. Having examined the wounds in his side, legs, head, and throat, the old hermit (a skilful leech) knelt down by the side of the vanquished one and said, 'Sir Knight, it is my painful duty to state to you that you are in an exceedingly dangerous condition, and will not probably survive.'

'Say you so, Sir Priest? then 'tis time I make my confession. Hearken you, Priest, and you, Sir Knight, whoever you be.'

Sir Ludwig (who, much affected by the scene, had been tying his horse up to a tree) lifted his visor and said, 'Gottfried of Godesberg! I am the friend of thy kinsman, Margrave Karl, whose happiness thou hast ruined; I am the friend of his chaste and virtuous lady, whose fair fame thou hast belied; I am the godfather of young Count Otto, whose heritage thou wouldst have appropriated. Therefore I met thee in deadly fight, and overcame thee, and have well-nigh finished thee. Speak on.'

'I have done all this,' said the dying man, 'and here, in my last hour, repent me. The Lady Theodora is a spotless lady; the youthful Otto the true son of his father—Sir Hildebrandt is not his father, but his *uncle*.'

'Gracious Buffo!' 'Celestial Bugo!' here said the hermit and the Knight of Hombourg simultaneously, clasping their hands.

'Yes, his uncle; but with the *bar-sinister* in his 'scutcheon. Hence he could never be acknowledged by the family; hence, too, the Lady Theodora's spotless purity (though the young people had been brought up together) could never be brought to own the relationship.'

'May I repeat your confession?' asked the hermit.

'With the greatest pleasure in life: carry my confession to the Margrave, and pray him give me pardon. Were there—a notary-public present,' slowly gasped the knight, the film of dissolution glazing over his eyes, 'I would ask—you—two—gentlemen to

23

witness it. I would gladly—sign the deposition—that is, if I
could wr-wr-wr-wr-ite!' A faint shuddering smile—a quiver, a
gasp, a gurgle—the blood gushed from his mouth in black
volumes. . . .

'He will never sin more,' said the hermit solemnly.

'May Heaven assoilzie him!' said Sir Ludwig. 'Hermit, he
was a gallant knight. He died with harness on his back, and
with truth on his lips : Ludwig of Hombourg would ask no other
death. . . .'

An hour afterwards the principal servants at the Castle of
Godesberg were rather surprised to see the noble Lord Louis trot
into the courtyard of the castle, with a companion on the crupper
of his saddle. 'Twas the venerable Hermit of Rolandseck, who,
for the sake of greater celerity, had adopted this undignified con-
veyance, and whose appearance and little dumpy legs might well
create hilarity among the 'pampered menials' who are always
found lounging about the houses of the great. He skipped off the
saddle with considerable lightness, however ; and Sir Ludwig,
taking the reverend man by the arm, and frowning the jeering
servitors into awe, bade one of them lead him to the presence of
His Highness the Margrave.

'What has chanced?' said the inquisitive servitor. 'The
riderless horse of Sir Gottfried was seen to gallop by the outer
wall anon. The Margrave's Grace has never quitted your Lord-
ship's chamber, and sits as one distraught.'

'Hold thy prate, knave, and lead us on!' And so saying, the
Knight and his Reverence moved into the well-known apartment,
where, according to the servitor's description, the wretched
Margrave sat like a stone.

Ludwig took one of the kind broken-hearted man's hands, the
hermit seized the other, and began (but on account of his great
age, with a prolixity which we shall not endeavour to imitate) to
narrate the events which we have already described. Let the
dear reader fancy, the while his Reverence speaks, the glazed eyes
of the Margrave gradually lighting up with attention ; the flush
of joy which mantles in his countenance—the start—the throb—
the almost delirious outburst of hysteric exultation with which,
when the whole truth was made known, he clasped the two
messengers of glad tidings to his breast, with an energy that
almost choked the aged recluse! 'Ride, ride this instant to the
Margravine—say I have wronged her, that it is all right, that she
may come back—that I forgive her—that I apologise, if you will'
—and a secretary forthwith despatched a note to that effect,
which was carried off by a fleet messenger.

'Now write to the Superior of the monastery at Cologne, and bid him send me back my boy, my darling, my Otto—my Otto of roses!' said the fond father, making the first play upon words he had ever attempted in his life. But what will not paternal love effect? The secretary (smiling at the joke) wrote another letter, and another fleet messenger was despatched on another horse.

'And now,' said Sir Ludwig playfully, 'let us to lunch. Holy hermit, are you for a snack?'

The hermit could not say nay on an occasion so festive, and the three gentles seated themselves to a plenteous repast; for which

the remains of the feast of yesterday offered, it need not be said, ample means.

'They will be home by dinner-time,' said the exulting father. 'Ludwig! reverend hermit! we will carry on till then.' And the cup passed gaily round, and the laugh and jest circulated, while the three happy friends sat confidently awaiting the return of the Margravine and her son.

But alas! said we not rightly at the commencement of a former chapter, that betwixt the lip and the raised wine-cup there is often many a spill? that our hopes are high, and often, too often, vain? About three hours after the departure of the first messenger, he returned, and with an exceedingly long face knelt down and presented to the Margrave a billet to the following effect :—

'CONVENT OF NONNENWERTH : *Friday Afternoon.*

'SIR,—I have submitted too long to your ill-usage, and am disposed to bear it no more. I will no longer be made the butt of your ribald satire, and the object of your coarse abuse. Last week you threatened me with your cane ! On Tuesday last you threw a wine-decanter at me, which hit the butler, it is true, but the intention was evident. This morning, in the presence of all the servants, you called me by the most vile abominable name, which Heaven forbid I should repeat ! You dismissed me from your house under a false accusation. You sent me to this odious convent to be immured for life. Be it so ! I will not come back, because, forsooth, you relent. Anything is better than a residence with a wicked, coarse, violent, intoxicated, brutal monster like yourself. I remain here for ever, and blush to be obliged to sign myself   THEODORA VON GODESBERG.

'*P.S.*—I hope you do not intend to keep all my best gowns, jewels, and wearing-apparel ; and make no doubt you dismissed me from your house in order to make way for some vile hussy, whose eyes I would like to tear out,   T. V. G.'

THIS singular document, illustrative of the passions of women at all times, and particularly of the manners of the early ages, struck dismay into the heart of the Margrave.

'Are her Ladyship's insinuations correct?' asked the hermit in a severe tone. 'To correct a wife with a cane is a venial, I may say a justifiable practice; but to fling a bottle at her is ruin, both to the liquor and to her.'

'But she sent a carving-knife at me first,' said the heart-broken husband. 'O jealousy, cursed jealousy, why, why did I ever listen to thy green and yellow tongue?'

'They quarrelled; but they loved each other sincerely,' whispered Sir Ludwig to the hermit; who began to deliver forthwith a lecture upon family discord and marital authority, which would have sent his two hearers to sleep, but for the arrival of the second messenger, whom the Margrave had despatched to Cologne for his son. This herald wore a still longer face than that of his comrade who preceded him.

'Where is my darling?' roared the agonised parent. 'Have ye brought him with ye?'

'N—no,' said the man, hesitating.

'I will flog the knave soundly when he comes,' cried the father, vainly endeavouring, under an appearance of sternness, to hide his inward emotion and tenderness.

'Please, your Highness,' said the messenger, making a desperate effort, 'Count Otto is not at the convent.'

'Know ye, knave, where he is?'

The swain solemnly said, 'I do. He is *there*.' He pointed as he spake to the broad Rhine, that was seen from the casement, lighted up by the magnificent hues of sunset.

'*There!* How mean ye *there?*' gasped the Margrave, wrought to a pitch of nervous fury.

'Alas! my good lord, when he was in the boat which was to

27

conduct him to the convent, he—he jumped suddenly from it, and is dr-dr-owned.'

'Carry that knave out and hang him!' said the Margrave, with a calmness more dreadful than any outburst of rage. 'Let every man of the boat's crew be blown from the mouth of the cannon on the tower—except the coxswain, and let him be——'

What was to be done with the coxswain, no one knows; for at that moment, and overcome by his emotion, the Margrave sank down lifeless on the floor.

CHAPTER VIII

THE CHILDE OF GODESBERG

It must be clear to the dullest intellect (if amongst our readers we dare venture to presume that a dull intellect should be found) that the cause of the Margrave's fainting fit, described in the last chapter, was a groundless apprehension on the part of that too solicitous and credulous nobleman regarding the fate of his beloved child. No, young Otto was *not* drowned. Was ever hero of romantic story done to death so early in the tale? Young Otto was *not* drowned. Had such been the case, the Lord Margrave would infallibly have died at the close of the last chapter; and a few gloomy sentences at its close would have denoted how the lovely Lady Theodora became insane in the convent, and how Sir Ludwig determined, upon the demise of the old hermit (consequent upon the shock of hearing the news), to retire to the vacant hermitage, and assume the robe, the beard, the mortifications of the late venerable and solitary ecclesiastic. Otto was *not* drowned, and all those personages of our history are consequently alive and well.

The boat containing the amazed young Count—for he knew not the cause of his father's anger, and hence rebelled against the unjust sentence which the Margrave had uttered—had not rowed many miles, when the gallant boy rallied from his temporary surprise and despondency, and determined not to be a slave in any convent of any order : determined to make a desperate effort for escape. At a moment when the men were pulling hard against the tide, and Kuno, the coxswain, was looking carefully to steer the barge between some dangerous rocks and quicksands, which are frequently met with in the majestic though dangerous river, Otto gave a sudden spring from the boat, and with one single flounce was in the boiling, frothing, swirling eddy of the stream.

Fancy the agony of the crew at the disappearance of their young lord! All loved him; all would have given their lives for him; but as they did not know how to swim, of course they

declined to make any useless plunges in search of him, and stood
on their oars in mute wonder and grief.   *Once*, his fair head and
golden ringlets were seen to arise from the water; *twice*, puffing
and panting, it appeared for an instant again; *thrice*, it rose but
for one single moment: it was the last chance, and it sunk, sunk,
sunk.   Knowing the reception they would meet with from their
liege lord, the men naturally did not go home to Godesberg, but,
putting in at the first creek on the opposite bank, fled into the
Duke of Nassau's territory; where, as they have little to do with
our tale, we will leave them.

But they little knew how expert a swimmer was young Otto.
He had disappeared, it is true: but why? because he *had dived*.

He calculated that his conductors would consider him drowned,
and the desire of liberty lending him wings (or we had rather say
fins, in this instance), the gallant boy swam on beneath the water,
never lifting his head for a single moment between Godesberg and
Cologne—the distance being twenty-five or thirty miles.

Escaping from observation, he landed on the *Deutz* side of the
river, repaired to a comfortable and quiet hostel there, saying he
had had an accident from a boat, and thus accounting for the
moisture of his habiliments, and while these were drying before a
fire in his chamber, went snugly to bed, where he mused, not
without amaze, on the strange events of the day.   'This morning,'
thought he, 'a noble, and heir to a princely estate—this evening
an outcast, with but a few bank-notes which my mamma luckily

gave me on my birthday. What a strange entry into life is this for a young man of my family! Well, I have courage and resolution : my first attempt in life has been a gallant and success-ful one; other dangers will be conquered by similar bravery.' And recommending himself, his unhappy mother, and his mis-taken father to the care of their patron saint, Saint Buffo, the gallant-hearted boy fell presently into such a sleep, as only the young, the healthy, the innocent, and the extremely fatigued, can enjoy.

The fatigues of the day (and very few men but would be fatigued after swimming well-nigh thirty miles under water) caused young Otto to sleep so profoundly, that he did not remark how, after Friday's sunset, as a natural consequence, Saturday's Phœbus illumined the world, ay, and sunk at his appointed hour. The serving-maidens of the hostel, peeping in, marked him sleeping, and blessing him for a pretty youth, tripped lightly from the chamber ; the boots tried haply twice or thrice to call him (as boots will fain), but the lovely boy, giving another snore, turned on his side, and was quite unconscious of the interruption. In a word, the youth slept for six-and-thirty hours at an elongation ; and the Sunday sun was shining, and the bells of the hundred churches of Cologne were clinking and tolling in pious festivity, and the burghers and burgheresses of the town were trooping to vespers and morning service when Otto awoke.

As he donned his clothes of the richest Genoa velvet, the astonished boy could not at first account for his difficulty in putting them on. 'Marry,' said he, 'these breeches that my blessed mother' (tears filled his fine eyes as he thought of her)— 'that my blessed mother had made long on purpose, are now ten inches too short for me. Whir-r-r! my coat cracks i' the back, as in vain I try to buckle it round me ; and the sleeves reach no farther than my elbows! What is this mystery? Am I grown fat and tall in a single night? Ah! ah! ah! ah! I have it.'

The young and good-humoured Childe laughed merrily. He bethought him of the reason of his mistake : his garments had shrunk from being five-and-twenty miles under water.

But one remedy presented itself to his mind ; and that we need not say was to purchase new ones. Inquiring the way to the most genteel ready-made clothes' establishment in the city of Cologne, and finding it was kept in the Minoriten Strasse, by an ancestor of the celebrated Moses of London, the noble Childe hied him towards the emporium ; but you may be sure did not neglect to perform his religious duties by the way. Entering the cathedral, he made straight for the shrine of St. Buffo, and, hiding himself behind a pillar there (fearing he might be recognised by the Archbishop, or any of his father's numerous friends in Cologne), he proceeded with his devotions, as was the practice of the young nobles of the age.

But though exceedingly intent upon the service, yet his eye could not refrain from wandering a *little* round about him, and he remarked with surprise that the whole church was filled with archers ; and he remembered, too, that he had seen in the streets numerous other bands of men similarly attired in green. On asking at the cathedral porch the cause of this assemblage, one of the green ones said (in a jape), 'Marry, youngster, *you* must be *green*, not to know that we are all bound to the castle of his Grace Duke Adolf of Cleves, who gives an archery meeting once a year, and prizes for which we toxophilites muster strong.'

Otto, whose course hitherto had been undetermined, now immediately settled what to do. He straightway repaired to the ready-made emporium of Herr Moses, and bidding that gentleman furnish him with an archer's complete dress, Moses speedily selected a suit from his vast stock, which fitted the youth to a *t*, and we need not say was sold at an exceedingly moderate price. So attired (and bidding Herr Moses a cordial farewell), young Otto was a gorgeous, a noble, a soul-inspiring boy to gaze on. A coat and breeches of the most brilliant pea-green, ornamented with a profusion of brass buttons, and fitting him with exquisite tightness, showed off a figure unrivalled for slim symmetry. His feet were covered with peaked buskins of buff leather, and a belt round his slender waist, of the same material, held his knife, his tobacco-pipe and pouch, and his long shining dirk ; which, though the adventurous youth had as yet only employed it to fashion wicket-bails, or to cut bread-and-cheese, he was now quite ready to use against the enemy. His personal attractions were enhanced by a neat white hat, flung carelessly and fearlessly on one side of his open smiling countenance ; and his lovely hair, curling in ten thousand yellow ringlets, fell over his shoulder like golden epaulettes, and down his back as far as the waist-buttons of his coat. I warrant me, many a lovely Cölnerinn looked after the handsome Childe with anxiety, and dreamed that night of Cupid under the guise of 'a bonny boy in green.'

So accoutred, the youth's next thought was, that he must supply himself with a bow. This he speedily purchased at the most fashionable bowyer's, and of the best material and make. It was of ivory, trimmed with pink ribbon, and the cord of silk. An elegant quiver, beautifully painted and embroidered, was slung across his back with a dozen of the finest arrows, tipped with steel of Damascus, formed of the branches of the famous Upas tree of Java, and feathered with the wings of the ortolan. These purchases being completed (together with that of a knapsack, dressing-case, change, etc.), our young adventurer asked where was the hostel at which the archers were wont to assemble ? and being informed that it was at the sign of the 'Golden Stag,' hied him to that house of entertainment, where, by calling for quantities of liquor and beer, he speedily made the acquaintance and acquired the goodwill of a company of his future comrades who happened to be sitting in the coffee-room.

After they had eaten and drunken for all, Otto said, addressing them, 'When go ye forth, gentles ? I am a stranger here, bound as you to the archery meeting of Duke Adolf. An ye will admit a youth into your company, 'twill gladden me upon my lonely way ?'

The archers replied, 'You seem so young and jolly, and you spend your gold so very like a gentleman, that we'll receive you in our band with pleasure. Be ready, for we start at half-past two !' At that hour accordingly the whole joyous company prepared to move, and Otto not a little increased his popularity among them by stepping out and having a conference with the landlord, which caused the latter to come into the room where the archers were assembled previous to departure, and to say, 'Gentlemen, the bill is settled !'—words never ungrateful to an archer yet : no, marry, nor to a man of any other calling that I wot of.

They marched joyously for several leagues, singing and joking, and telling of a thousand feats of love and chase and war. While thus engaged, some one remarked to Otto, that he was not dressed in the regular uniform, having no feathers in his hat.

'I dare say I will find a feather,' said the lad, smiling.

Then another gibed because his bow was new.

'See that you can use your old one as well, Master Wolfgang,' said the undisturbed youth. His answers, his bearing, his generosity, his beauty, and his wit, inspired all his new toxophilite friends with interest and curiosity, and they longed to see whether his skill with the bow corresponded with their secret sympathies for him.

An occasion for manifesting this skill did not fail to present itself soon—as indeed it seldom does to such a hero of romance as young Otto was. Fate seems to watch over such : events occur to them just in the nick of time ; they rescue virgins just as ogres are on the point of devouring them ; they manage to be present at Court and interesting ceremonies, and to see the most interesting people at the most interesting moment ; directly an adventure is necessary for them, that adventure occurs : and I, for my part, have often wondered with delight (and never could penetrate the mystery of the subject) at the way in which that humblest of romance heroes, Signor Clown, when he wants anything in the Pantomime, straightway finds it to his hand. How is it that—suppose he wishes to dress himself up like a woman, for instance, that minute a coalheaver walks in with a shovel-hat that answers for a bonnet: at the very next instant a butcher's lad passing with a string of sausages and a bundle of bladders unconsciously helps Master Clown to a necklace and a *tournure*, and so on through the whole toilet? Depend upon it there is something we do not wot of in that mysterious overcoming of circumstances by great individuals : that apt and wondrous conjuncture of *the Hour and the Man ;* and so, for my part, when I heard the above remark of one of the archers, that Otto had never a feather in his bonnet, I felt sure that a heron would spring up in the next sentence to supply him with an *aigrette*.

And such indeed was the fact: rising out of a morass by which the archers were passing, a gallant heron, arching his neck, swelling his crest, placing his legs behind him, and his beak and red eyes against the wind, rose slowly, and offered the fairest mark in the world.

'Shoot, Otto,' said one of the archers.   'You would not shoot just now at a crow because it was a foul bird, nor at a hawk because it was a noble bird ; bring us down yon heron : it flies slowly.'

But Otto was busy that moment tying his shoe-string, and Rudolf, the third best of the archers, shot at the bird and missed it.

'Shoot, Otto,' said Wolfgang, a youth who had taken a liking to the young archer : 'the bird is getting further and further.'

But Otto was busy that moment whittling a willow-twig he had just cut.   Max, the second best archer, shot and missed.

'Then,' said Wolfgang, 'I must try myself : a plague on you, young springald, you have lost a noble chance !'

Wolfgang prepared himself with all his care, and shot at the bird.   'It is out of distance,' said he, 'and a murrain on the bird !'

Otto, who by this time had done whittling his willow-stick (having carved a capital caricature of Wolfgang upon it), flung the twig down and said carelessly, 'Out of distance !   Pshaw ! We have two minutes yet,' and fell to asking riddles and cutting jokes ; to the which none of the archers listened, as they were all engaged, their noses in air, watching the retreating bird.

'Where shall I hit him ?' said Otto.

'Go to,' said Rudolf, 'thou canst see no limb of him : he is no bigger than a flea.'

'Here goes for his right eye !' said Otto ; and stepping forward

THREE=AND=SIXPENNY LIBRARY

By C. M. YONGE and C. R. COLERIDGE
Strolling Players

By VARIOUS WRITERS

Hogan, M.P.
Flitters, Tatters, and the Counsellor
The New Antigone
Tim
Memories of Father Healy
CUTCLIFFE HYNE.—The "Paradise" Coal-Boat
CANON ATKINSON.—The Last of the Giant Killers
R. H. BARHAM. — The Ingoldsby Legends
HAWLEY SMART. — Breezie Langton
ANTHONY TROLLOPE.—The Three Clerks
SIR H. LYTTON BULWER.— Historical Characters
RICHARD JEFFERIES.—The Dewy Morn
FRANK BUCKLAND.—Curiosities of Natural History. 4 vols.
MRS. HUMPHRY WARD.— Miss Bretherton
D. C. MURRAY and H. HERMAN. — He fell among Thieves
LUCAS MALET.—Mrs. Lorimer
LANOE FALCONER.— Cecilia de Noël
M.M'LENNAN.—MuckleJock, and other Stories
MAJOR GAMBIER PARRY.— The Story of Dick
S. R. LYSAGHT.—The Marplot
SIR H. M. DURAND.—Helen Treveryan
MARCHESA THEODOLI.— Under Pressure
W. C. RHOADES.—John Trevennick

E. C. PRICE —In the Lion's Mouth
BLENNERHASSET AND SLEEMAN.—Adventures in Mashonaland
W. FORBES-MITCHELL. — Reminiscences of the Great Mutiny
REV. J. GILMORE. — Storm Warriors
LORD REDESDALE.—Tales of Old Japan
SIR S. BAKER.—True Tales for my Grandsons
HENRY KINGSLEY. — Tales of Old Travel
W. P. FRITH, R.A.—My Autobiography
CAMILLE ROUSSET. — Recollections of Marshal Macdonald
CHARLES WHITEHEAD.— Richard Savage
F. A. MIGNET.—Mary Queen of Scots
F. GUIZOT.—Oliver Cromwell
M. R. MITFORD.— Literary Recollections
REV. R. H. D. BARHAM.—Life of R. H. Barham
——— Life of Theodore Hook
Biographies of Eminent Persons   Vol. I.
      ,,   ,,   II.
      ,,   ,,   III.
      ,,   ,,   IV.
      ,,   ,,   V.
Annual Summaries. Vol. I.
      ,,   ,,   II.
Masson's French Dictionary
Shakespeare's Works. Vol. I.
      ,,   ,,   II.
      ,,   ,,   III.

MACMILLAN AND CO., LTD., LONDON

2 8.03

THREE-AND-SIXPENNY LIBRARY

MACMILLAN AND CO., LTD., LONDON

THREE=AND=SIXPENNY LIBRARY

By Mrs. PARR

Dorothy Fox | Loyalty George
Adam and Eve | Robin

By W. CLARK RUSSELL

Marooned | A Strange Elopement

By Sir WALTER SCOTT

The Large-type Illustrated Border Edition of THE WAVERLEY NOVELS
In 24 volumes

Waverley | Peveril of the Peak
Guy Mannering | Quentin Durward
The Antiquary | St. Ronan's Well
Rob Roy | Redgauntlet
Old Mortality | The Betrothed, and The
The Heart of Midlothian | Talisman
A Legend of Montrose, and | Woodstock
the Black Dwarf | The Fair Maid of Perth
The Bride of Lammermoor | Anne of Geierstein
Ivanhoe   The Abbot | Count Robert of Paris, and
The Monastery   Kenilworth | The Surgeon's Daughter
The Pirate | Castle Dangerous, Chronicles
The Fortunes of Nigel | of the Canongate, etc.

By J. H. SHORTHOUSE

John Inglesant | The Countess Eve
Sir Percival | A Teacher of the Violin
Little Schoolmaster Mark | Blanche, Lady Falaise

By W. M. THACKERAY

Reprints of the First Editions, with all the Original Illustrations,
Facsimiles of Wrappers, etc.

Vanity Fair | Book of Snobs, Miss Tickle-
The History of Pendennis | toby's Lectures, History of
The Newcomes | the next French Revolution,
The Virginians | A Little Dinner at Timmins',
The History of Henry Esmond | etc.
Barry Lyndon and Catherine | The Yellowplush Correspond-
Paris and Irish Sketch Books | ence, Diary and Letters of
Christmas Books | James de la Pluche, History
Burlesques, From Cornhill | of Samuel Titmarsh and the
to Grand Cairo, and Juve- | Great Hoggarty Diamond,
nilia | and Contributions to the
  | Constitutional [and Public
  | Ledger]

MACMILLAN AND CO., LTD., LONDON

THREE=AND=SIXPENNY LIBRARY

CHARLES KINGSLEY—*continued*

Sermons on National Subjects | Discipline, and other Sermons
Sermons for the Times | Westminster Sermons
Good News of God | All Saints' Day, and other
The Gospel of the Penta- | Sermons
teuch, etc. |

By MAARTEN MAARTENS

An Old Maid's Love | God's Fool
The Greater Glory | The Sin of Joost Avelingh
My Lady Nobody | Her Memory

By A. E. W. MASON

The Courtship of Morrice | The Philanderers
Buckler | Miranda of the Balcony

By F. D. MAURICE

Lincoln's Inn Sermons. Vol. I. | Prophets and Kings
,, ,, II. | Patriarchs and Lawgivers
,, ,, III. | Gospel of Kingdom of Heaven
,, ,, IV. | Gospel of St. John
,, ,, V. | Epistles of St. John
,, ,, VI. | Friendship of Books
Sermons Preached in Country | Prayer Book and Lord's
Churches. | Prayer
Christmas Day | Doctrine of Sacrifice
Theological Essays | Acts of the Apostles

By D. CHRISTIE MURRAY

Aunt Rachel | The Weaker Vessel
Schwartz | John Vale's Guardian

By W. E. NORRIS

Thirlby Hall | Bachelor's Blunder

By Mrs. OLIPHANT

Neighbours on the Green | Sir Tom
Joyce | The Heir-Presumptive, etc.
Kirsteen | A Country Gentleman
A Beleaguered City | A Son of the Soil
Hester | The Second Son
He that Will Not when He | The Wizard's Son
May | The Curate in Charge
The Railway Man | Lady William
Marriage of Elinor | Young Musgrave

MACMILLAN AND CO., LTD., LONDON

THREE=AND=SIXPENNY LIBRARY

By W. WARDE FOWLER

A Year with the Birds
Tales of the Birds
More Tales of the Birds

Summer Studies of Birds and Books

By THOMAS HARDY

Tess of the D'Urbervilles
Far from the Madding Crowd
The Mayor of Casterbridge
A Pair of Blue Eyes
Two on a Tower
The Return of the Native
The Woodlanders
Jude the Obscure
The Trumpet-Major
The Hand of Ethelberta
A Laodicean

Desperate Remedies
Wessex Tales
Life's Little Ironies
A Group of Noble Dames
Under the Greenwood Tree
The Well Beloved
Wessex Poems and other Verses
Poems of the Past and the Present

By BRET HARTE

Cressy: A Novel
A First Family of Tasajara

The Heritage of Dedlow Marsh

By THOMAS HUGHES

Tom Brown's Schooldays
Tom Brown at Oxford

Scouring of the White Horse
Alfred the Great

By HENRY JAMES

A London Life
The Aspern Papers, etc.

The Tragic Muse

By ANNIE KEARY

A York and a Lancaster Rose
Castle Daly
Janet's Home

Oldbury
A Doubting Heart
Nations around Israel

By CHARLES KINGSLEY

Westward Ho! | Hypatia
Yeast | Alton Locke
Two Years Ago
Hereward the Wake | Poems
The Heroes
The Water Babies
Madam How and Lady Why
At Last | Prose Idylls
Plays and Puritans
The Roman and the Teuton

Sanitary and Social Lectures
Historical Lectures and Essays
Scientific Lectures and Essays
Literary and General Lectures
The Hermits | Glaucus
Village and Town and Country Sermons
The Water of Life, and other Sermons

MACMILLAN AND CO., LTD., LONDON

THREE-AND-SIXPENNY LIBRARY

F. MARION CRAWFORD—*continued*

Khaled
The Witch of Prague
The Three Fates
Marion Darche
Children of the King
Katharine Lauderdale
Pietro Ghisleri
Don Orsino

The Ralstons
Casa Braccio
Adam Johnstone's Son
A Rose of Yesterday
Taquisara | Corleone
Via Crucis. A Romance of
the Second Crusade
In the Palace of the King

By Sir H. CUNNINGHAM

The Heriots | Wheat and Tares | The Coeruleans

By CHARLES DICKENS

Reprints of the First Editions, with the Illustrations; and Biographical
and Bibliographical Introductions by Charles Dickens the Younger

Pickwick Papers
Oliver Twist
Nicholas Nickleby
Martin Chuzzlewit
The Old Curiosity Shop
Barnaby Rudge
Dombey and Son

Christmas Books
Sketches by Boz
David Copperfield
American Notes
Letters of Charles Dickens
Bleak House | Little Dorrit
Tale of Two Cities

'ENGLISH MEN OF LETTERS,' 13 vols.

I. Chaucer, Spenser, Dryden
II. Milton, Goldsmith, Cowper
III. Byron, Shelley, Keats
IV. Wordsworth, Southey, Landor
V. Lamb, Addison, Swift
VI. Scott, Burns, Coleridge
VII. Hume, Locke, Burke
VIII. Defoe, Sterne, Hawthorne
IX. Fielding, Thackeray, Dickens
X. Gibbon, Carlyle, Macaulay
XI. Sydney, De Quincey, Sheridan
XII. Pope, Johnson, Gray
XIII. Bacon, Bunyan, Bentley

By DEAN FARRAR

Seekers after God
Eternal Hope
The Fall of Man
Witness of History to Christ
Silence and Voices of God

In the Days of thy Youth
Saintly Workers
Ephphatha
Mercy and Judgment
Sermons in America

By ARCHIBALD FORBES

Barracks, Bivouacs, and Battles | Souvenirs of Some Continents

MACMILLAN AND CO., LTD., LONDON

THREE=AND=SIXPENNY LIBRARY

By ROLF BOLDREWOOD

Robbery under Arms
The Miner's Right
The Squatter's Dream
A Sydney-side Saxon
A Colonial Reformer
Nevermore
A Modern Buccaneer
The Sealskin Cloak

Plain Living
The Crooked Stick
My Run Home
Old Melbourne Memories
War to the Knife
Romance of Canvas Town
Babes in the Bush
In Bad Company and other Stories

By ROSA NOUCHETTE CAREY

Nellie's Memories
Wee Wifie
Barbara Heathcote's Trial
Robert Ord's Atonement
Wooed and Married
Heriot's Choice
Queenie's Whim
Mary St. John
Not Like Other Girls
For Lilias
Uncle Max

Only the Governess
Lover or Friend?
Basil Lyndhurst
Sir Godfrey's Granddaughters
The Old, Old Story
Mistress of Brae Farm
Mrs. Romney, and But Men Must Work
Other People's Lives
Rue with a Difference
Herb of Grace

By EGERTON CASTLE

Consequences
The Bath Comedy
The Pride of Jennico

The Light of Scarthey
La Bella, and others
"Young April"

By HUGH CONWAY

A Family Affair

Living or Dead

By Mrs. CRAIK

Olive
The Ogilvies
Agatha's Husband
The Head of the Family
Two Marriages
The Laurel Bush
My Mother and I

Miss Tommy
King Arthur: Not a Love Story
About Money, and other Things
Concerning Men, and other Papers

By F. MARION CRAWFORD

Mr. Isaacs
Dr. Claudius
A Roman Singer
Zoroaster
A Tale of a Lonely Parish

Marzio's Crucifix
Paul Patoff
With the Immortals
Greifenstein | Sant' Ilario
Cigarette-Maker's Romance

MACMILLAN AND CO., LTD., LONDON

THE WORKS OF
CHARLES DICKENS

A Reprint of the First Edition, with the Illustrations, and
Introductions, Biographical and Bibliographical,
by CHARLES DICKENS the Younger.

Crown 8vo. **3/6** *each volume.*

THE PICKWICK PAPERS. With 50 Illustrations.

OLIVER TWIST. With 27 Illustrations.

NICHOLAS NICKLEBY. With 44 Illustrations.

MARTIN CHUZZLEWIT. With 41 Illustrations.

THE OLD CURIOSITY SHOP. With 97 Illustrations.

BARNABY RUDGE. With 76 Illustrations.

DOMBEY AND SON. With 40 Illustrations.

CHRISTMAS BOOKS. With 65 Illustrations.

SKETCHES BY BOZ. With 44 Illustrations.

AMERICAN NOTES and PICTURES FROM ITALY.
    With 4 Illustrations.

DAVID COPPERFIELD. With 40 Illustrations.

BLEAK HOUSE. With 43 Illustrations.

LITTLE DORRIT. With 40 Illustrations.

THE LETTERS OF CHARLES DICKENS.

A TALE OF TWO CITIES. Illustrated.

MACMILLAN AND CO., LTD., LONDON.

THE WORKS OF THACKERAY

Reprints of the First Editions, with all the Original Illustrations, and with Facsimiles of Wrappers, etc.
Crown 8vo. 3s. 6d. each.

VANITY FAIR.	HISTORY OF PENDENNIS.
THE NEWCOMES.	HISTORY OF HENRY ESMOND.

THE VIRGINIANS.
BARRY LYNDON ; AND CATHERINE.
PARIS AND IRISH SKETCH BOOKS.
CHRISTMAS BOOKS
BURLESQUES ; FROM CORNHILL TO GRAND CAIRO; AND JUVENILIA.

Volumes in the Press.

BOOK OF SNOBS ; MISS TICKLETOBY'S LECTURES ; HISTORY OF THE NEXT FRENCH REVOLUTION, ETC.

THE YELLOWPLUSH CORRESPONDENCE; DIARY AND LETTERS OF JEAMES DE LA PLUCHE; HISTORY OF SAMUEL TITMARSH AND THE GREAT HOGGARTY DIAMOND; AND CONTRIBUTIONS TO THE CONSTITUTIONAL [AND PUBLIC LEDGER].

CRITICAL PAPERS IN LITERATURE.

CRITICAL PAPERS IN ART; STUBBS'S CALENDAR; BARBER COX.

LOVEL THE WIDOWER, AND OTHER STORIES.

THE FITZ-BOODLE PAPERS; MEN'S WIVES; THE SECOND FUNERAL OF NAPOLEON, AND OTHER SKETCHES.

LECTURES ON THE ENGLISH HUMOURISTS OF THE EIGHTEENTH CENTURY ; THE FOUR GEORGES ; CHARITY AND HUMOUR, ETC.

SKETCHES AND TRAVELS IN LONDON ; MR· BROWN'S LETTERS TO A YOUNG MAN ABOUT TOWN ; THE PROSER, ETC.

BALLADS AND VERSES; A LITTLE DINNER AT TIMMINS'S; MISCELLANEOUS CONTRIBUTIONS TO *PUNCH*.

THE ADVENTURES OF PHILIP, AND A SHABBY GENTEEL STORY.

MACMILLAN AND CO., LTD., LONDON.

I tended her by night and day,
  But when the sportsman stray'd
Along the silent harvest-field,
  Death stole my village-maid.

Now winter's come, with hollow voice,
  I hear the howling wind
Ring through the savage naked woods,
  All gloomy like my mind.
O spring! come not again to me,
  By her I would be laid,
For what are birds or flow'rs to me,
  Without my village-maid.

                                T. M.

THE END

Printed by R. & R. CLARK, LIMITED, *Edinburgh.*

seems to say—cop. copy! cop. copy! but, by his own horns, he shall have none this time.—There! good ink—hiss on the fire awhile. Well?'—'If you please, sir, they say if you don't send more copy they'll not be able to get the work out, and if you please, they say the last you've sent's nonsense!'—'Indeed!' —'Yes, sir, they do.'—'Well, you must fetch me some ink; I've got none.'—'Why, if you please, when I come for the last copy you'd nearly a bottleful,—I shin'd it, sir!'—'Rascal, go along and fetch more, or I'll kick you downstairs! Cop. copy! cop. copy! by Jupiter, he shall have no more cop. copy to-night for his impudence. A villain!—to take notice of my ink. Now, I'll lock my door, creep into bed, and if he cries copy! copy! until his throat's sore, he shall have none until I've taken my rest.'

· T. M.

ORIGINAL POETRY.

SONG.

I MET her in the early month
 Of blossom-laden spring;
When budding trees were lightly rob'd,
 And larks soar'd high to sing.
We wandered where the primrose grew,
 Deep in a silent glade,
And vow'd that naught save death should part
 Me and my village-maid.

When summer came with laughing days,
 And soft blue-hanging skies,
Which threw a gladness all around,
 As did her softer eyes;
Again we sought the twilight woods,
 Where hazels form'd a shade;
The ring-dove and the singing brook
 Pleas'd my sweet village-maid.

When autumn came in solemn gold,
 And yellow leaves were strown;
'Twas then death mark'd my village-maid,
 Alas! to be his own.

—yaw, yaw, yoyaw! What a wonderful system is man's,—no doing without sleep. Never did Satan arise with greater reluctance from his brimstone bed, to quell some riot infernal, than I rise now to furnish my devil with copy. Let's see,—I have not a line composed. Before me stands a pile of MS. which in time will out-top Olympus—it has all been published. As I opened my mouth just now to yawn, the printer's devil looked as if he would jump down my throat for 'more copy.' 'Wait a minute, my boy, while I write something. (*Aside.*) I wish your neck had been broken before you'd reach'd here.' Well, I must begin. 'The sun went down behind the dark-waving woods of Burton, amid masses of broken clouds, that roll'd wildly along, like war-steeds broken loose from the starry stables of heaven.'—'Here, my boy, take this.'—'Is this all, sir? I shall be back again in a minute for more.'—'Well, take that first, and begone; I shall have more ready ere you return.' There, thank God! I've got rid of that urchin once more. What were the ghosts that flitted with shadowy wings around King Richard's tent compared to this substantial devil? He was born with the word 'copy' upon his tongue. O for some pious divine to *lay* him, as they *lay* other devils when they arise,—in the Red Sea, or anywhere, so that I never see his demoniacal features in future. O mercy! here he comes again.—'More copy, sir, please!'—'The devil copy you! why, you must have lost the other; it never can have been set up in this time.'—'O dear, sir, when I got there, two on 'em wanted copy, and it seem'd no more to 'em than a nut would be to a whale for breakfast.'—'Where did I leave off, my boy, I have quite forgotten what I was writing.'—'If you please, sir, you left off at heaven, sir.'—'Humph! and I must begin again at the other place now you've come; I have no more knowledge as to what I was writing about than this pen. Well, yaw! yaw! yoyaw! the-e-y must have co-o-o-py,—there, I feel all the better for that. Heaven—well :'—'In heaven we shall have no crying out for copy (yaw—yaw!), in heaven we shall never feel sleepy, in heaven we shall have no proofs to correct, no punctuation to study, no silly *Tales of the Sea* to review, no Tories to attack,—no— no.'—'Here, my boy, tell the compositor to be particular in the pointing of this, as it's a climax!'—'Yes, sir.'

'O, what a blessing I've got rid of this ever-haunting spirit once more : yaw! yaw! yoyaw! yo-o-o-ah! there—hark! What again! I've only had time to place my feet comfortably upon the fender, (which once formed part of the tire of a waggon-wheel,) stretch my arms out three times, gape four, and rub my eyes five, before I again hear the devil upon the stairs. Every step he takes

MR. CROCKFORD.

GOOD readers, great Crockford you here may behold,
The fishmonger famous, whose fishes are gold;
His eye of a whiting, and mouth of a cod,
　Give a touch of his old fishy trade to his looks,
But they know, who can tell you a wink from a nod,
　That he now sticks to poultry, to pigeons, and rooks.
Yet he still makes a cast, and not seldom a haul,
　Still angles for flats, and still nets what he can;
And shows, every night, 'mid his shoal great and small,
　The trick how a gudgeon is made of a man.

L. E. U.

THE DEVIL TO PAY—A SKETCH.

I HAVE just now swallowed my supper, and am looking with vacant eye upon the fire,—the only little rest which my jaded mind has enjoyed for the last twenty-four hours. Hark! I know his foot,—it is the printer's devil come again for 'more copy':

THE HISTORY OF THE FISH

THE HOG-BACKED TROUT